Disney PRINCESS

THINGS to MAKE and DO

AUTUMN PUBLISHING

AUTUMN
PUBLISHING

Published in 2021
First published in the UK by Autumn Publishing
An imprint of Igloo Books Ltd
Cottage Farm, NN6 0BJ, UK
Owned by Bonnier Books
Sveavägen 56, Stockholm, Sweden
www.igloobooks.com

0821 001
2 4 6 8 10 9 7 5 3 1
ISBN 978-1-83903-043-7
Printed and manufactured in China

CONTENTS

BELLE'S BIO

Personality: Inquisitive, genuine and brave.

About: Belle's previously quiet life took an unexpected turn when she agreed to stay at the Beast's castle to save her father. Always seeing the best in people, she was able to help break the curse on the Beast and his enchanted servants. Belle also loves reading and can often be found with her nose in a good book.

Have a go!

Write a story about your favourite Disney Princess.

BELLE'S ENCHANTED BOOKMARK

YOU WILL NEED:

Scissors
Sheet of card
Glue

INSTRUCTIONS:

1. Ask an adult to help you cut out the bookmark panels.
2. Stick one panel onto a piece of card
3. Cut around the panel that is stuck onto the card.
4. Stick the second bookmark panel onto the other side of the cut-out card – it should fit perfectly.
5. Great job! You now have your own Belle bookmark.

Bookmark Panels:

© Disney

© Disney

WHY NOT TRY?

On the page opposite is an awesome Princess quiz! Throughout the book, there are lots of different Princess quizzes you can try. Why not challenge yourself, your friends and your family to see who can get the most correct answers?

THE *BEAUTY AND THE BEAST* QUIZ

1. Which country does Belle come from?

a) Germany b) France c) Norway d) Spain

2. What is the name of Belle's horse?

a) Philippe b) Chestnut c) Hugo d) Harry

3. What job does Maurice, Belle's father, do?

a) Chef b) Dentist c) Inventor d) Vet

4. What type of object is Cogsworth?

a) Teapot b) Plate c) Table d) Clock

5. What colour is Belle's dress when she dances with the Beast?

a) Green b) Yellow c) Red d) Blue

6. What is Belle's favourite hobby?

a) Reading b) Dancing c) Cooking
d) Running

7. Who expects Belle to marry him?

a) Gary b) Gavin c) Gaston d) Gareth

8. What animals chase both Maurice and Belle?

a) Crows b) Bears c) Wolves d) Tigers

Turn the page upside down to see the answers!
1:b 2:a 3:c 4:d 5:b 6:a 7:c 8:c

BELLE'S MAGICAL
Quinoa Porridge

Just like overnight oats, this straight-from-the-fridge breakfast magically comes together while you sleep. Lightly sweetened with honey and topped with fresh berries – this is the perfect morning treat.

INGREDIENTS:

175g cooked quinoa

175ml coconut milk

100g unsweetened chopped dried cherries

2 tablespoons desiccated coconut

2 teaspoons honey

75g mixed fresh berries

2 tablespoons toasted flaked almonds

1 banana, sliced

2 large strawberries

DIRECTIONS:

1 In a medium bowl, stir together the quinoa, coconut milk, cherries, desiccated coconut and honey. Refrigerate overnight.

2 Place a strawberry on the end of a fork, leaf side down. Ask an adult to help you carefully cut staggered slits around the perimeter of the berry to form rose petals as shown on the right. Use the edge of the knife to pull back the petals slightly and give them dimension. Repeat with the other strawberry.

3 Remove the porridge from the fridge and add a few tablespoons of water if it is too thick. Divide the porridge between the two bowls, then garnish each with half the banana slices, fresh berries and almonds. Top each with a strawberry rose.

JASMINE'S BIO

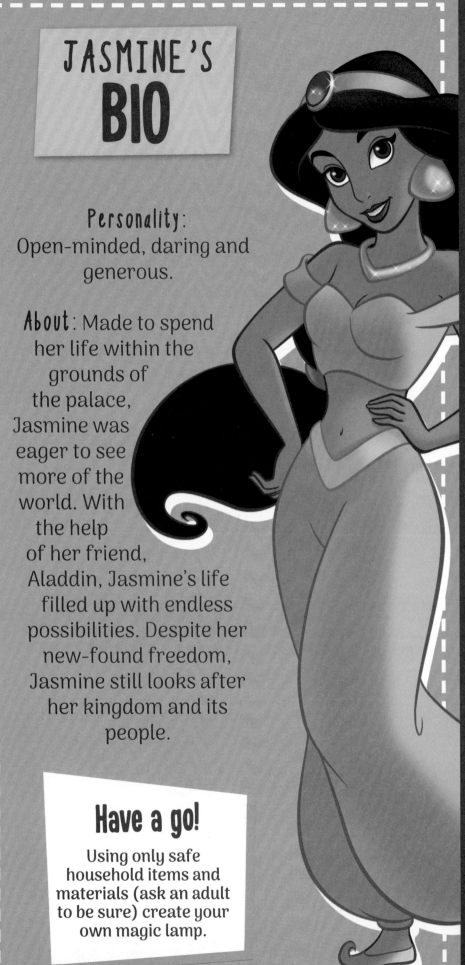

Personality: Open-minded, daring and generous.

About: Made to spend her life within the grounds of the palace, Jasmine was eager to see more of the world. With the help of her friend, Aladdin, Jasmine's life filled up with endless possibilities. Despite her new-found freedom, Jasmine still looks after her kingdom and its people.

Have a go!

Using only safe household items and materials (ask an adult to be sure) create your own magic lamp.

JASMINE'S CELEBRATION BUNTING

YOU WILL NEED:

Scissors
String/Ribbon
EXTRAS:
Coloured paper/card

INSTRUCTIONS:

1. Ask an adult to help you cut out the bunting panels.

2. Carefully cut out the smaller holes on each panel.

3. Pull the string/ribbon through the holes on each bunting panel until they are all in a row.

4. If you want to make more bunting, cut out triangle shapes from paper/card, decorate them, then add to the row.

Bunting Panels:

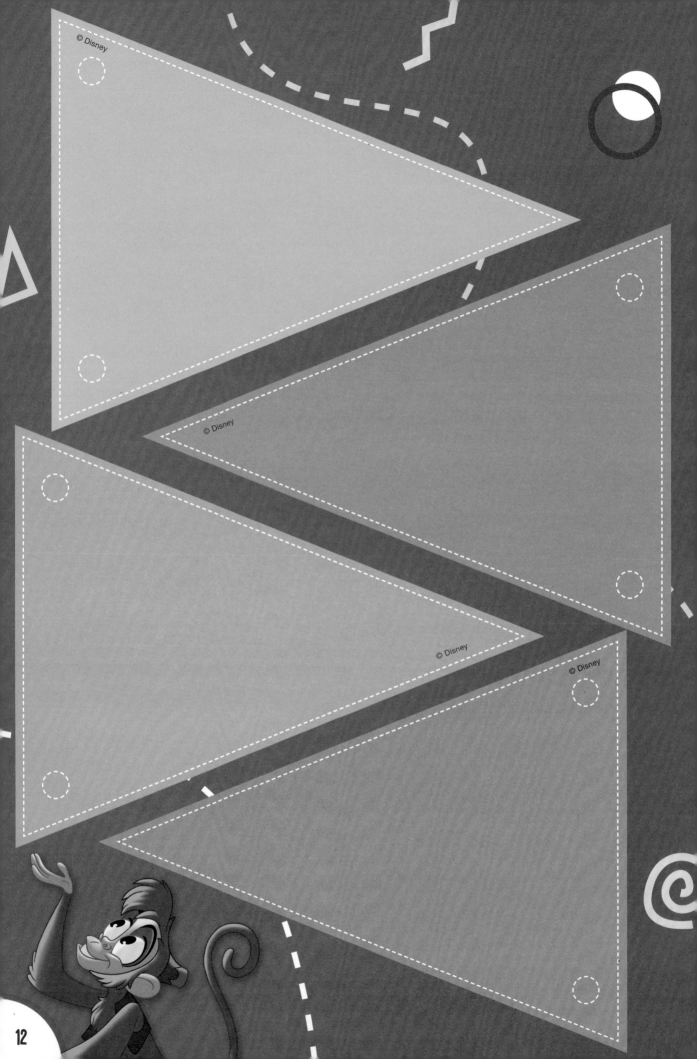

© Disney

© Disney

© Disney

© Disney

12

THE ALADDIN QUIZ

1. What type of animal is Jasmine's pet, Rajah?

a) Lion b) Tiger c) Monkey d) Parrot

2. If Jasmine chooses to marry, what will it be for?

a) Power b) A bigger palace c) Money d) Love

3. Who is the Sultan of Agrabah to Jasmine?

a) Father b) Uncle c) Brother d) Grandfather

4. What does Aladdin pretend to be when he meets Jasmine at the palace?

a) A prince b) A sorcerer c) A sultan d) A genie

5. Where does Jasmine first meet Aladdin?

a) The palace b) The marketplace c) The desert
d) The Cave of Wonders

6. Who is the main villain in *Aladdin*?

a) Abu b) Aladdin c) Jafar d) Razoul

7. What is the name of Jafar's parrot?

a) Ian b) Iago c) Polly d) Percy

8. What colour is the Genie?

a) Green b) Yellow c) Red d) Blue

Turn the page upside down to see the answers!

1:b 2:d 3:a 4:a 5:b 6:c 7:b 8:d

MAGIC CARPET
Flatbread

Put a whole new twist on pizza night with this tasty *Aladdin*-inspired flatbread. Start with a base made of houmous in place of tomato sauce, then top with warm falafel, olives, fresh veggies and feta – like a wish come true! Don't forget to ask an adult to help.

INGREDIENTS:

1 packet chilled pizza dough

Flour, for dusting

225g houmous

6 pieces shop-bought falafel

50g black olives

75g plum tomatoes, halved

1 yellow pepper, sliced

50g crumbled feta

2 tablespoons chopped fresh parsley

DIRECTIONS:

1 On a lightly floured surface, roll out the pizza dough into a long rectangle. Use kitchen scissors to fringe each end, as shown.

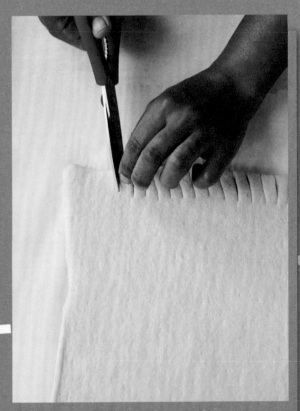

2 Fully bake the dough according to the packet directions. Reheat the falafel according to the packet instructions.

3 Spread the houmous onto the flatbread. Create a pattern on top with the falafel, olives, tomatoes and peppers. Garnish with the feta and parsley. Serve immediately.

TIANA'S BIO

Personality: Ambitious, confident and talented.

About: After a magical adventure through the Bayou, Tiana discovered her recipe for success required more than hard work, being a skilful cook and a knowledge of business – it needed love, too! Never one to back down, Tiana overcame all the obstacles in her path to finally achieve her dream of opening her own restaurant.

Have a go!

Cut a hand-sized hole in the side of a shoe box, or a similar sized box with a lid (ask an adult to help when using scissors). Place items inside and get your friends and family to guess what's in there through touch alone!

THE PRINCESS AND THE FROG QUIZ

1. Where does Tiana live?

a) New Orleans **b)** New York **c)** New Jersey
d) New England

2. Which fictional country is Prince Naveen from?

a) Miltonia **b)** Maldonado **c)** Maldoland **d)** Maldonia

3. What is the name of Tiana's restaurant?

a) Bayou Beignets **b)** Tiana's Palace
c) The Lily Pad **d)** Mardi Gras Magic

4. What do Tiana and Naveen magically turn into?

a) Alligators **b)** Fireflies **c)** Frogs **d)** Snakes

5. What is the name of Tiana's best friend?

a) Joy **b)** Laura **c)** Charlotte **d)** Jennifer

6. What instrument does Louis the Alligator play?

a) Trumpet **b)** Bassoon **c)** Guitar **d)** Tuba

7. Who is the main villain in *Princess and the Frog*?

a) Captain Voodoo **b)** Dr. Facilier **c)** Bayou Bob
d) Swamp Sam

8. What does Charlotte ask Tiana to make 500 of?

a) Cookies **b)** Pretzels **c)** Jam Tarts **d)** Beignets

Turn the page upside down to see the answers!
1:a 2:d 3:b 4:c 5:c 6:a 7:b 8:d

CHEF TIANA'S
WATER LILY APRON

Tiana loves to cook! When you and someone special are baking wonderful treats together, you'll both need an apron to protect your clothes.

YOU WILL NEED:

Plain apron
Masking tape
Pencil
Scissors

Card
Sponge
Brushes
Fabric paints

1 Tape an ironed apron to a table with some card and newspaper underneath.

2 Draw a simple water lily petal shape onto card and also a lily pad shape. Ask an adult to help you cut them out.

3 Sponge some white paint onto the petal shaped card, then press it down in the centre of the apron. Repeat this until you have a flower, then leave to dry.

4

Sponge some pale green paint onto the card lily pad. Print it onto the apron, then flip it over to make another lily pad shape, then leave to dry.

5

Add a printed pattern to the centre of the flower with a strip of card with paint added to one edge, then paint yellow dots to finish the flower!

Top Tip

As a special touch, write your name on the apron!

SNOW WHITE'S BIO

Personality: Caring, optimistic and sweet-natured.

About: Snow White's kindness and positivity allow her to face any situation, however bad, and always find a solution. Although the Evil Queen tries to take advantage of Snow White's good qualities, her friends are able to save the day and rescue Snow White from an eternal sleep.

Have a go!

Go on an indoor scavenger hunt. Can you find seven different items beginning with 'D'?

1. Which of these isn't the name of a Dwarf?

a) Grumpy b) Doc c) Stinky d) Sleepy

2. What flavour pie does Snow White bake?

a) Gooseberry b) Pear c) Cherry d) Cottage

3. How many of the Dwarfs' names begin with the letter 'D'?

a) One b) Two c) Three d) Four

4. What does the Evil Queen wish to be?

a) Cleverest of All b) Funniest of All c) Strongest of All
d) Fairest of All

5. What poisoned fruit does Snow White bite?

a) Banana b) Watermelon c) Apple d) Orange

6. Who helps Snow White clean the Seven Dwarfs' cottage?

a) The animals b) The Huntsman c) The Evil Queen
d) The Dwarfs

7. What does the Evil Queen turn herself into before she visits Snow White?

a) One of the Dwarfs b) A rabbit c) An old hag
d) The Huntsman

8. What type of mine do the Seven Dwarfs work in?

a) A gold mine b) A diamond mine c) A silver mine
d) An apple mine

Turn the page upside down to see the answers!

1:c 2:a 3:b 4:d 5:c 6:a 7:c 8:b

SNOW WHITE'S CASTLE
JEWELLERY STAND

A castle is not just a castle, it is also a wonderful way to display your Princess fashion crafts and jewellery!

YOU WILL NEED:

Cardboard box (small)

Cardboard tubes different sizes

A circle of cardboard for a balcony

Coloured card for doors and windows

Pencil

Glue

Small jar

Scissors

Masking tape

Paints

Brushes

Sequins/gems

1 Arrange the tubes around a small box into a good castle shape. Cut the tubes if you need to so they vary in height. Don't glue them together yet.

2 Cut out some circles from card to make the turrets, they need to be around 14cm diameter for smaller turrets and 20cm diameter for the bigger ones. Cut the circles in half so you have semicircles.

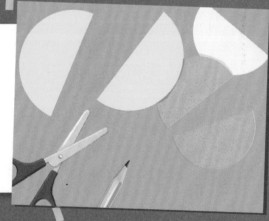

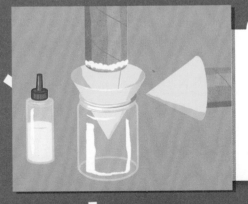

3 Curl the semicircles into cone shapes and stick masking tape along the edge. Place each cone upside down into a small jar (to stop it rolling around) then glue the tube inside it.

4 Glue the turrets together around the box. To make a balcony, glue a circle of cardboard on top of the largest turret, then stick a smaller turret on top. Leave the glue to dry, then paint your castle in a beige colour to make it look like a castle wall.

5 While the paint dries, cut out small windows and a door from the coloured card. Then, glue them in place. Glue sequins for extra sparkle. Then display your most precious jewellery from the turrets.

Top Tip

Remember to always ask an adult for help when using scissors!

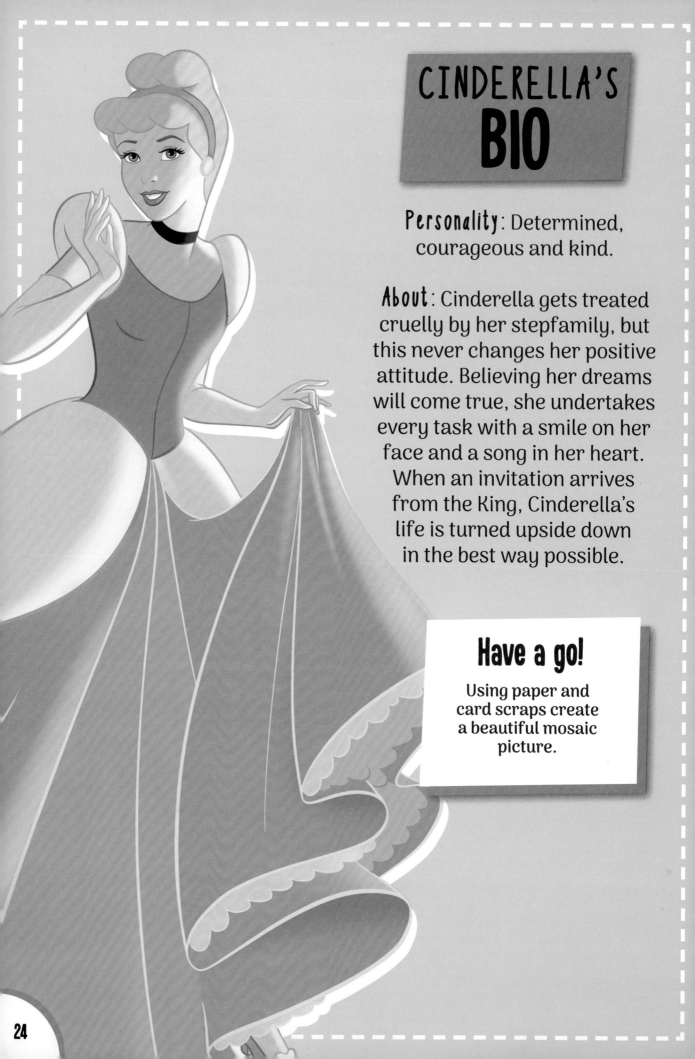

CINDERELLA'S BIO

Personality: Determined, courageous and kind.

About: Cinderella gets treated cruelly by her stepfamily, but this never changes her positive attitude. Believing her dreams will come true, she undertakes every task with a smile on her face and a song in her heart. When an invitation arrives from the King, Cinderella's life is turned upside down in the best way possible.

Have a go!

Using paper and card scraps create a beautiful mosaic picture.

THE CINDERELLA QUIZ

1. What is the name of Cinderella's stepmother?

a) Lady Remain **b)** Lady Tremaine
c) Lady Retrain **d)** Lady Complain

2. Who is looking for a wife at the royal ball?

a) The King **b)** The Grand Duke
c) The Prince **d)** The Fairy Godmother

3. What kind of carriage does the Fairy Godmother create?

a) Broccoli **b)** Sweet Potato **c)** Cabbage **d)** Pumpkin

**4. Cinderella has two stepsisters. One is Drizella.
Who is the other?**

a) Anastasia **b)** Annabelle **c)** Abigail **d)** Ariadna

5. What are the mice turned into by the Fairy Godmother?

a) Guards **b)** Footmen **c)** Horses **d)** Cats

6. What are Cinderella's magical slippers made from?

a) Wood **b)** Cotton **c)** Plastic **d)** Glass

7. What sort of animal is Lucifer?

a) Cat **b)** Mouse **c)** Horse **d)** Dog

8. At what time does the Fairy Godmother's magic wear off?

a) Ten o'clock **b)** Eleven o'clock **c)** Midnight **d)** One o'clock

Turn the page upside down to see the answers!
1:b 2:c 3:d 4:a 5:c 6:d 7:a 8:c

CINDERELLA'S
SOCK MICE FRIENDS

The mice are Cinderella's best friends. Now you can make cute mice for you and your friends to play with.

1

Push some cotton wool into a sock so it is around one third full.

2

Tie up the end of the sock with a long piece of wool – this will be the tail. Ask an adult to help you trim off the open end of the sock.

3

Cut two felt circles, approximately 4cm in diameter. Add glue to one edge of the circles and then pinch the edges together into ear shapes. Leave to dry.

4

Cut small felt circles for the eyes and nose, then glue them onto the sock along with the ears and wool whiskers.

Top Tip

These mice look so cute placed on a pillow when your friends have made their bed!

MERIDA'S BIO

Personality: Brave, responsible and strong.

About: Headstrong and independent, Merida wants to do things her own way. Although her mother tries to teach her how the clans expect a princess to act, Merida would much rather be riding in the woods and practising archery. She also has a strong interest in the local myths of her land.

Have a go!

Doodle a picture of you and your family.

MAKE YOUR OWN CLAN FLAG

INSTRUCTIONS:

1. Glue the short stick across the long stick, around 2cm down from the top. The two together should look like a cross.

2. Decorate the clan flag with your unique design.

3. Ask an adult to help you cut out the clan flag.

4. Glue the flag's top edge along the short stick.

5. Using sticky tack, secure the bottom of the long stick on to the milk bottle top. Your clan flag will now be able to stand on its own for you to display proudly.

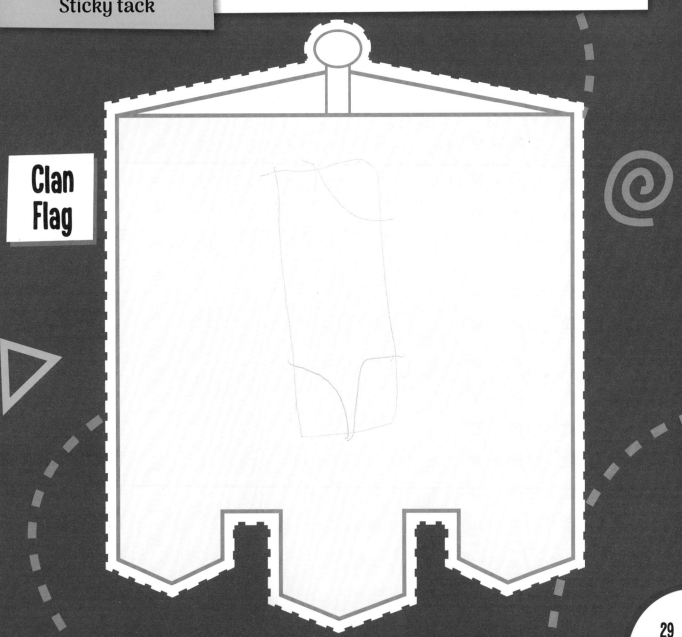

Clan Flag

WHY NOT TRY?

Use the clan flag as a template to help you make even more amazing flags. Or create flag shapes of your very own!

© Disney

THE *BRAVE* QUIZ

1. Where does Merida come from?

a) France b) England c) Spain d) Scotland

2. Which of these activities is Merida highly skilled at?

a) Swimming b) Archery c) Sewing d) Cooking

3. What animal does the spell turn Merida's mother into?

a) Bear b) Wolf c) Horse d) Frog

4. What is Merida's mother's name?

a) Emma b) Elizabeth c) Erin d) Elinor

5. How many brothers does Merida have?

a) Two b) Three c) Four d) Five

6. What clan does Merida belong to?

a) DunBroch b) Dingwall c) Macintosh d) Macguffin

7. What does Merida cut after an argument with her mother?

a) Her dress b) A tablecloth c) A tapestry d) Her hair

8. What does Elinor eat that turns her into a bear?

a) Bread b) Cake c) Apple pie d) Fish

Turn the page upside down to see the answers!

1:d 2:b 3:a 4:d 5:b 6:a 7:c 8:b

WILL-O-THE-WISP
Meringues

If you've never made meringues, you'll be pleasantly surprised to discover how simple they are to bake. The mix-and-match look can be achieved by piping both rosettes and swirls with a star nozzle, but using a plain nozzle will produce a similarly magical look. Don't forget to ask an adult to help.

Prep	Cook	Makes
30 mins	4 hrs (includes baking and drying time)	36 meringues

INGREDIENTS:

4 egg whites, at room temperature
1/2 teaspoon cream of tartar
1/4 teaspoon peppermint extract
225g caster sugar
Blue food colouring

DIRECTIONS:

1 Heat oven to 110°C (90 fan) | 225°F | gas 0.25. Line two baking sheets with parchment paper.

2 Using an electric whisk, beat the egg whites until foamy. Add the cream of tartar and 1 tablespoon of sugar. Continue to beat, adding the remaining sugar 1 tablespoon at a time, until stiff peaks form, about 6 minutes. Add the peppermint extract, tint with blue food colouring, and beat until well blended.

3 Spoon the meringue into a piping bag fitted with a large star nozzle. Pipe 5 - 8cm rosettes and swirls onto each prepared baking sheet, spacing them 3cm apart. Bake for 2 hours. Do not open the oven door. Turn off the heat and leave the meringues inside the oven to continue to dry out for at least 2 hours. Store in an airtight container until ready to serve.

MOANA'S BIO

Personality: Bold, compassionate and respectful.

About: Moana has always been drawn to the open ocean, and the adventure that awaits on the waves. Despite her father banning any sailing beyond the reef, events force Moana to break that rule. With the guidance of Gramma Tala, Moana is determined to save her island home and find her true destiny.

Have a go!

Using only safe household items and materials (ask an adult to be sure) build a hand-sized raft that floats on water.

THE MOANA QUIZ

1. Where does Moana live?

a) Motunui **b)** Motumaui **c)** Mononui **d)** Monomaui

2. What is the name of Moana's father?

a) Chief Bui **b)** Chief Sui **c)** Chief Tui **d)** Chief Wui

3. What does demigod Maui need to get back from Tamatoa?

a) Spear **b)** Fish hook **c)** Paddle **d)** Necklace

4. What is Moana's chicken called?

a) Heihei **b)** Pua **c)** Maui **d)** Te Fiti

5. What is Moana's quest?

a) Return the watch of Te Fiti **b)** Return the soul of Te Fiti
c) Return the song of Te Fiti **d)** Return the heart of Te Fiti

6. What are Tamatoa's favourite kind of things?

a) Soft **b)** Rough **c)** Bouncy **d)** Shiny

7. During the film, what animal does Maui not change into?

a) Chicken **b)** Shark **c)** Iguana **d)** Hawk

8. What does Moana discover about her ancestors?

a) They were gods **b)** They were voyagers
c) The could shapeshift **d)** They could fly

Turn the page upside down to see the answers!

1:a 2:c 3:b 4:a 5:d 6:d 7:a 8:b

MOANA'S
STARRY PEN TUBE

Make a tube to hold pens, pencils or crayons for yourself or to give as a gift. This one is designed like the night sky.

YOU WILL NEED:

Cardboard tube with lid
Fine sandpaper
Black acrylic paint
Paintbrush
White glue and brush

Glitter: gold, silver
Scrap paper
Sequins and star stickers

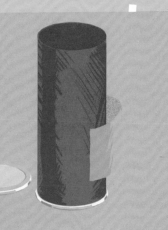

1 Lightly rub the tube all over with sandpaper. This will help the paint stick better to the tube.

2 Cover the tube in black acrylic paint. Let dry, then apply another coat. Let the tube dry thoroughly.

3 Brush some glue onto the tube then sprinkle the glitter over the top. Shake off the excess glitter onto a piece of scrap paper.

4 Add the star stickers. Glue a row of sequins around the top and bottom of the tube, or anywhere to make your pen tube shimmer.

Top Tip

Stars shine brightly at night. This would make a wonderful gift for someone who you think is a skilled wayfinder!

MULAN'S BIO

Personality: Fearless, clever and loyal.

About: Mulan struggles to be true to herself while keeping her family happy. To save her father's life, Mulan joins the army disguised as a man. In doing so, Mulan discovers her true purpose. By helping defeat the invading army and rescuing the Emperor, Mulan brings her family honour.

Have a go!

Dress up as your favourite Princess using just old clothes. Can anyone guess which Princess you are?

THE *MULAN* QUIZ

1. **What does Mulan tell everyone her name is when she's disguised as a man?**

a) Zing b) Bing c) Wing d) Ping

2. **What does Shang challenge the recruits to recover from the top of a pole?**

a) An arrow b) A cricket c) A sword d) A doll

3. **What is Cri-Kee?**

a) An unlucky beetle b) A singing bee c) A lucky cricket
d) An invisible bird

4. **What colour is Mulan's dragon-friend Mushu?**

a) Blue b) Red c) Purple d) Grey

5. **Who does Mulan take the place of when she joins the army?**

a) Her father b) Her mother c) Her grandmother d) Her dog

6. **What does Mulan bring to her family?**

a) A stray cat b) Pizza c) Honour d) A cup of tea

7. **What is Mulan's family name?**

a) Li b) Fa c) Yao d) Chi

8. **What is fired at Shan-Yu on the roof of the Emperor's palace?**

a) Cannon ball b) Confetti c) Arrows
d) Giant firework rocket

Turn the page upside down to see the answers!

1:d 2:a 3:c 4:b 5:a 6:c 7:b 8:d

MULAN'S
FRIENDSHIP BRACELETS

Mulan's friends helped her save the Emperor! Show your friends how much you like them with an awesome friendship band.

YOU WILL NEED:

4 strands of embroidery thread, each 50cm long: 2 mauve, 1 pink and 1 purple (or your choice of colours)

1 large bead
4 medium-sized beads

1 Take the 4 strands of embroidery thread and knot them together, 20cm from one end.

2 Thread the large bead on the bracelet and push it up as far as the knot.

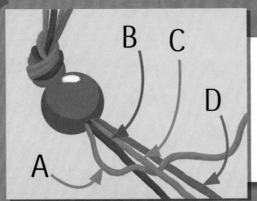

3 Spread out the 4 strands so that the 2 mauve strands are first and third from the left. Put A over B, under C and over D. Pull A gently to tighten the weave.

4

Continue weaving B over C, under D and over A, working over, under, over, under. Pull gently to tighten before starting on the next left-hand strand.

5

Continue weaving until you are about 8cm from the end, then tie the woven strands into a knot, leaving the ends loose.

6

Thread a medium-sized bead onto each of the 4 loose strands and tie a knot to keep it in place.

Top Tip

When making a bracelet, choose colours and beads that remind you of the friend you're making it for.

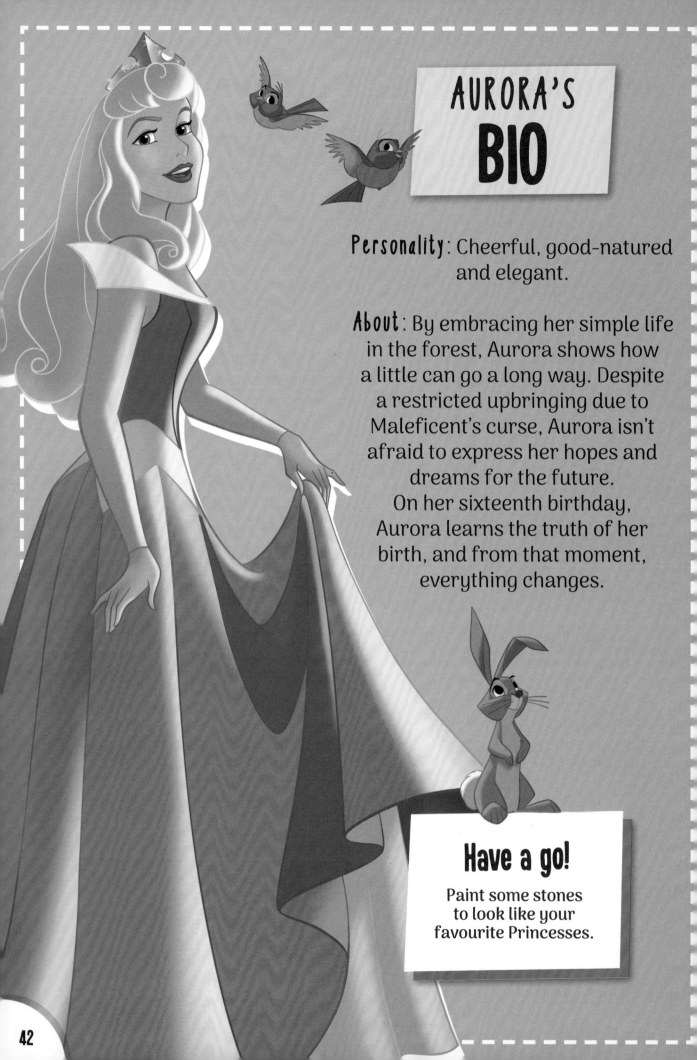

AURORA'S BIO

Personality: Cheerful, good-natured and elegant.

About: By embracing her simple life in the forest, Aurora shows how a little can go a long way. Despite a restricted upbringing due to Maleficent's curse, Aurora isn't afraid to express her hopes and dreams for the future.
On her sixteenth birthday, Aurora learns the truth of her birth, and from that moment, everything changes.

Have a go!

Paint some stones to look like your favourite Princesses.

THE SLEEPING BEAUTY QUIZ

1. Who curses Aurora at her christening?

a) Fauna b) Flora c) Merryweather d) Maleficent

2. Which of the below are not fairies?

a) Merryweather b) Fauna c) Flora d) King Stefan

3. What does the name 'Aurora' mean?

a) The dawn b) The night c) Midday d) Twilight

4. On which birthday is Aurora cursed to prick her finger?

a) Fourteenth b) Fifteenth c) Sixteenth d) Seventeenth

5. What does Aurora prick herself on?

a) A thorn b) A spindle c) A sewing needle d) A pin

6. Who defeats Maleficent?

a) King Stefan b) The fairies c) Aurora d) Prince Phillip

7. What does Maleficent transform into?

a) A dragon b) A horse c) A crow d) A cat

8. What happens to Aurora when she pricks her finger?

a) She can't stop dancing b) She keeps singing
c) She falls into an eternal sleep
d) She turns into a cake

Turn the page upside down to see the answers!

1:d 2:d 3:a 4:c 5:b 6:d 7:a 8:c

AURORA'S HEART
PILLOWCASE

The good fairies are making Aurora a surprise. Sleep in style with this pillowcase fit for a princess.

YOU WILL NEED:

Plain white pillowcase

Heart shape cut from card

Pencil

Cork

Fabric paint

Saucer

1 Push a piece of card inside the pillowcase. Tape the edges to a covered work surface. Place a cut-out card heart in the middle of the pillowcase to use as a guide for printing.

2 Pour a small amount of fabric paint into a saucer. Dip a cork into the paint. Use it to print dots around the card heart shape. Dip the cork back into the paint after every two or three dots.

3

Use the end of a pencil dipped into another colour to print smaller dots inside the bigger dots.

4

Take away the card heart and print another smaller heart shape using different colours inside the bigger heart. Leave to dry thoroughly, then put a pillow inside the case. Sweet dreams.

Top Tip

Why not try other shapes, like a wonderful star design.

SLEEPING BEAUTY

Doughnut Cake

Prep 1hr 10 mins   **Cook** 5 mins   **Serves** 7

The topsy-turvy layers of this lofty cake are impressive, but even the good fairy Fauna could pull it off. Making it is all about the assembly – no baking required! – and some artful, but easy, dipping and icing action. Don't forget to ask an adult to help.

INGREDIENTS:

- 1kg ready-to-roll fondant icing
- 7 chocolate doughnuts
- Blue food colouring
- Yellow food colouring
- 50g chocolate chips
- 1 pretzel/bread stick
- 2 large marshmallows
- Pink cake candles

DIRECTIONS:

1   Set a wire rack over a baking sheet. Place 500g of fondant in a microwave-safe bowl. Warm at full power for 1 minute. Stir the fondant and continue to heat in 10-second bursts until completely melted and runny. Double-dip the doughnuts in the fondant and place on the rack to let the fondant set.

2   Combine two thirds of the remaining fondant with any left in the bowl. Heat once more as described in Step 1. Blend in several drops of blue food colouring, then transfer to a piping bag fitted with a medium plain nozzle. Pipe drips onto the doughnuts, as shown. Use a toothpick to smooth any clumps of the fondant as needed. Let set.

3   Meanwhile, place the chocolate chips in a microwave-safe bowl. Warm at full power for 30 seconds. Stir, then heat in 10-second bursts until melted. Use a pastry brush or mini spatula to coat the pretzel/bread stick with chocolate, then place on a sheet of parchment paper to let the chocolate set.

4 Use fondant to secure a doughnut to your serving platter. Stack the doughnuts slightly askew, as shown. If needed, use bamboo skewers to secure the doughnuts as they are stacked. Simply poke a skewer through several doughnuts to hold them in place and trim the end to conceal.

5 Heat the remaining white fondant as described in Step 1, then blend with several drops of yellow food colouring. Transfer half the fondant to a piping bag fitted with a small star nozzle. Pipe bunting around the top doughnut and dots of fondant where the candles will be placed.

6

To construct the broomstick, make a slit in the top of one of the marshmallows. Use fondant to attach the uncut end to the other marshmallow.

Fit the tip of the pretzel/bread stick inside the slit marshmallow, then position the other end of the stick between the top two doughnuts, as shown.

Attach the base of the marshmallow stack to the serving platter, then use a grass piping nozzle and the remaining yellow fondant to pipe lines over the marshmallows for the straw of the broom.

POCAHONTAS' BIO

Personality: Caring, agile and intelligent.

About: Pocahontas believes in listening to her heart and following her own path. She often talks with nature, and takes advice from the ancient tree Grandmother Willow. Pocahontas bravely stands up for what she believes in, with her selflessness creating peace between her tribe and the settlers.

Have a go!

When you're next on a walk with your family, go on a nature hunt. Look for a stick, two stones and three different types of leaf. (Always check with an adult before you pick anything up.)

POCAHONTAS DOOR HANGER

YOU WILL NEED:

Scissors

Piece of card

Glue

INSTRUCTIONS:

1. Ask an adult to help you cut out the door hanger panels.

2. Stick one panel onto a piece of card

3. Cut around the panel that is stuck onto the card.

4. Stick the second door hanger panel onto the other side of the cut-out card – it should fit perfectly.

5. You now have your very own door hanger.

Door Hanger Panels:

THIS ROOM BELONGS TO

THIS ROOM BELONGS TO

© Disney

© Disney

THE *POCAHONTAS* QUIZ

1. What is the name of the tree Pocahontas goes to for advice?

a) Grandmother Willow **b)** Grandfather Willow
c) Mother Willow **d)** Aunt Willow

2. What is Pocahontas' hummingbird friend called?

a) Whizzy **b)** Speedy **c)** Meeko **d)** Flit

3. What year is *Pocahontas* set?

a) 1607 **b)** 1707 **c)** 1807 **d)** 1907

4. What item did Meeko steal from John Smith's bag?

a) Coins **b)** Compass **c)** Canteen **d)** Map

5. What is Governor Ratcliffe's dog called?

a) Patrick **b)** Rover **c)** Percy **d)** Baxter

6. What advice is Pocahontas given?

a) Embrace your dreams **b)** Look to the stars
c) Be kind **d)** Listen with your heart

7. What is Governor Ratcliffe looking for?

a) Diamonds **b)** Gold **c)** Spices **d)** Corn

**8. What is the name of the person John Smith rescues
in the storm?**

a) Thomas **b)** Steven **c)** Christopher **d)** Michael

Turn the page upside down to see the answers!

1:a 2:d 3:a 4:b 5:c 6:d 7:b 8:a

51

POCAHONTAS

Feather Pops

Prep	Cook	Makes
30 mins	10 mins	6 pops

Fashioned after Pocahontas' feathered jewellery, these crisp lollipops are made with pastry. The icing in this bake is white, but you can add a few drops of edible colour if you like. Don't forget to ask an adult to help.

INGREDIENTS:

1 egg

Flour, for dusting

1 packet shortcrust pastry

100g icing sugar

2 tablespoons coconut milk

SPECIAL EQUIPMENT:

6 (15cm) lollipop sticks

10-12cm feather cookie cutter

1 toothpick/cocktail stick

DIRECTIONS:

1 Heat the oven to 200°C (180 fan) | 400°F | gas 6. Line a baking sheet with parchment paper.

2 Whisk the egg with 1 tablespoon water. On a lightly floured surface, roll out the pastry dough to a 6mm thickness. Use the feather cookie cutter to cut the dough into 12 feathers. Use a spatula to transfer half the feathers to the prepared baking sheet. Brush each with the egg wash and press a lollipop stick in the centre. Sandwich each with a plain feather by gently pressing it on top.

3 Bake the pops until golden around the edges, about 10 minutes. Use a spatula to transfer the pops to a wire rack to cool completely.

4 Sift the icing sugar into a small bowl. Stir in the coconut milk 2 teaspoons at a time until you have a smooth, spreadable icing. Ice each pop, then let the icing set. Use a toothpick to etch a line down the centre of each feather.

ARIEL'S
BIO

Personality: Curious, free-spirited and adventurous.

About: Ariel longs to know more about the human world that lives above the waves of her under-the-sea home. She is passionate and stands by her decisions. After her deal with Ursula goes wrong, the young princess holds strong, and proves she's capable of achieving anything.

Have a go!

How many items can you fit inside a matchbox, or similar sized box?

1. What is Ariel?

a) A shark b) A mermaid c) A seagull d) A fish

2. Who does Ariel save from drowning?

a) Prince Eric b) Grimsby c) Ursula d) King Triton

3. What does Ariel give up when she signs Ursula's contract?

a) Her dinglehopper b) Her hair c) Her sight d) Her voice

4. What is the name of Ariel's crab-friend who conducts an orchestra?

a) Flounder b) Scuttle c) Sebastian d) Vanessa

5. What animal are Ursula's minions, Flotsam and Jetsam?

a) Eels b) Great white sharks c) Clownfish d) Crabs

6. What is a dinglehopper?

a) A knife b) A spoon c) A fork d) A plate

7. Where does Ursula keep Ariel's voice?

a) In a shell necklace b) In a treasure chest
c) In a coat pocket d) In a purse

8. Which of these is not one of Ariel's sisters?

a) Attina b) Aquata c) Atlanta d) Alana

Turn the page upside down to see the answers!

1:b 2:a 3:d 4:c 5:a 6:c 7:a 8:c

55

ARIEL'S PRECIOUS
DISPLAY CASE

Ariel has many trinkets and treasures. To present them and keep them safe she has made her own display case. Make your own, it's easy and looks very special!

YOU WILL NEED:

Some small boxes
Glue
Paints

Paintbrush
Glitter
Scissors

1

Glue the boxes together. Ask an adult to help you trim the edges first if they need to be made smaller. Leave to dry.

2

Paint the outside of the boxes. Leave to dry.

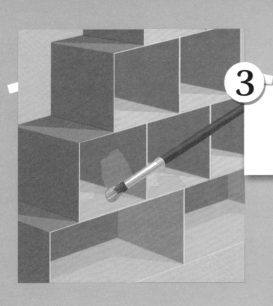

3 Paint the inside using a different colour. Leave to dry.

4 Tip the boxes over on one side and brush with glue and sprinkle with glitter. Do the same on the other side and on the top.

Top Tip

Put your most treasured item at the top of your case, and show it off properly!

RAPUNZEL'S BIO

Personality: Creative, inquisitive and devoted.

About: Despite life stuck in a tower, Rapunzel has been able to find her creative side, and expresses herself through a variety of skills, including painting and music. Yet, it is her curious nature that leads her to leave the tower to see the floating lights and finally discover who she really is.

Have a go!
Draw a self-portrait.

RAPUNZEL'S SUNNY MOBILE

YOU WILL NEED:
Scissors

Glue

2 lollipop sticks

Cocktail stick or toothpick

Coloured card

Coloured string

INSTRUCTIONS:
1. Make a cross with the two lollipop sticks and tie them together in the middle with some coloured string.

2. Cut out and glue the mobile pieces onto coloured card.

3. Cut around the pieces on the card and make a hole on each piece where marked (using the cocktail stick/ toothpick).

4. Thread a piece of string through the holes for each piece.

5. Tie the other end of the string to the sticks, using different lengths to hang each piece.

6. Tie a new piece of string to the centre of the sticks, then tie the other end to wherever you want to hang the mobile.

Mobile Pieces:

59

THE *TANGLED* QUIZ

1. Who kidnapped Rapunzel when she was a baby?

a) Father Gothel **b)** Mother Gothel

c) Brother Gothel **d)** Grandmother Gothel

2. Where did Rapunzel's magical power originally come from?

a) A flower **b)** A tree **c)** A bush **d)** A lake

3. What does Rapunzel's magical hair do when she sings?

a) It falls out **b)** It grows **c)** It glows **d)** It gets shorter

4. Where has Mother Gothel been keeping Rapunzel?

a) In a cottage **b)** In a boat **c)** In a dungeon **d)** In a tower

5. What does Rapunzel hit Flynn Rider over the head with?

a) A frying pan **b)** A rolling pin **c)** A paintbrush **d)** A crown

6. Who helps Flynn Rider steal the royal crown?

a) The Blabbington Brothers **b)** The Flabbington Brothers

c) The Stabbington Brothers **d)** The Yabbington Brothers

7. What is the name of the horse who is determined to capture Flynn?

a) Minimus **b)** Midimus **c)** Ultimus **d)** Maximus

8. What colour does Rapunzel's hair turn when it's cut?

a) Red **b)** Pink **c)** Black **d)** Brunette

Turn the page upside down to see the answers!

1:b 2:a 3:c 4:d 5:a 6:c 7:d 8:d

RAPUNZEL'S
BRAIDED BUNS

Edible flowers made of almonds and jam, and a dough that's filled with citrusy orange zest, make these twisted buns a festive spring snack. Serve them as a part of a big breakfast spread or alongside a hot cup of tea.

Prep	Cook	Makes
30 mins	1 hr (includes cooling and decorating time)	10

INGREDIENTS:

450g strong white bread flour

3 tablespoons sugar

3 teaspoons baking powder

1 teaspoon fine sea salt

250ml whole milk

3 tablespoons vegetable oil

2 teaspoons orange zest

2 large eggs

125g strawberry or raspberry jam

25g flaked almonds

DIRECTIONS:

1 Heat the oven to 200°C (180 fan) | 400°F | gas 6 and line a baking sheet with parchment paper. In a large bowl, whisk together the flour, sugar, baking powder and salt. In another bowl, whisk together the milk, oil, orange zest and one egg. Add one third of the wet ingredient mixture into the dry ingredients and stir to combine. Repeat twice, stirring until fully combined between each addition.

2 Turn the dough out onto a lightly floured surface and knead until smooth. Divide the dough into 10 equal portions. Working with one portion at a time, divide it into thirds and roll each piece into a 30cm rope. Pinch the ropes together at one end and braid, as shown. Transfer to the prepared baking sheet. Repeat with the remaining dough.

3 In a small bowl, whisk together the remaining egg and 1 tablespoon water. Brush the braids with egg wash, then bake until golden, about 10 minutes. Transfer to a wire rack to cool.

4 Spoon the jam into a ziplock bag and snip off a corner. Pipe a dollop of jam onto a braid, then embellish with almond petals, pressing them into the jam, as shown. Repeat, adding two or more almond flowers to each bun. Serve immediately.

RAPUNZEL'S BRIGHT
ROOM TIDY

YOU WILL NEED:

Round cardboard
waste basket
Roll of gift wrap
Scissors
White glue diluted with
equal amount of water
Paintbrush

Waste-paper baskets can be beautiful. Cover yours in some brightly coloured gift wrap. There's no need to hide your basket any more!

1 Choose gift wrap that you like. Cut a piece a bit larger than the container. Wrap the paper around the container and glue it in place.

Top Tip

Ask an adult about recycling the rubbish in your basket once it's full.

2 Ask an adult to help you make small snips in the top and bottom edges, fold them over and glue them down.